INSTANT ART
for
BIBLE
WORKSHEETS

Book Two

Compiled by
David Thatcher

Drawn by
Arthur Baker

PALM TREE

Acknowledgements

Special thanks to Rebecca Thatcher,
Heather Thompson and Brian Gale,
who all contributed some of the original
ideas.

First published 1989 in Great Britain by
PALM TREE PRESS
Rattlesden
Bury St Edmunds, Suffolk IP30 0SZ

ISBN 0 86208 126 2

© 1989 Palm Tree Press
    (See note about copyright in the Introduction.)

Cover and design by Arthur Baker
Typesetting by Barry Sarling, Rayleigh, Essex
Printed by the Five Castles Press, Ipswich, Suffolk

Introduction

The first book of *Instant Art for Bible Worksheets* was published in 1988 and has proved so successful that we have lost no time in putting together another collection!

As in Book One, these worksheets are intended to be a resource for a variety of applications: family services, Sunday schools, mid-week clubs, holiday clubs and for use in day schools. They have been designed so that children of varying ages and abilities can use them at their own level.

The sheets have been born out of, and developed in, the regular family services of a local group of Christians in Rustington, West Sussex. Here there is one meeting each week where the whole family worships together — babies in prams through to grand-parents. Each meeting is flexible and open to the leading of the Holy Spirit, but there is a basic framework. A time of lively praise and worship is usually followed by teaching specifically aimed at the children: this might include pictures, a filmstrip or drama. Whilst the teaching is being developed further for the adults, the children are given a worksheet reinforcing the teaching. The children look forward to the worksheets, which have the added advantage of keeping them reasonably quiet! None of the adults needs to leave the group to look after the children.

This pattern has been found to be most successful, and we believe that many other groups of Christians might welcome the opportunity to use the worksheets which have developed from the Rustington experience. The sheets are intended to be used in conjunction with, and not in place of, an accompanying talk.

• day school use
The worksheets lend themselves to follow-up work from a school or class assembly or a class lesson, for which they can be adapted, if necessary.

For the infant age group, the word search puzzles could either be deleted altogether or replaced by a simple word exercise. For the junior age group, the picture could be replaced by comprehension questions, multi-choice answer questions or similar exercises.

• photocopy/cut out
Unlike some of the titles in the 'Instant Art' series, this book has been compiled as a collection of single page worksheets, the assumption being that users will reproduce a particular page (as a unit) in the quantities they require. However, individual items could be combined with other material and used in whatever way is most helpful. Our aim continues to be to provide material that is versatile and flexible in use.

As before, the pages have been printed on one side only to give the best possible quality of reproduction from a photocopier. The book's format allows it to be placed flat on the photocopier.

• Bible editions
We have used either the *New International Version* or the *Good News Bible*, the two editions which our research shows are the most commonly used by children.

• contents
A list of the worksheets contained in this collection, together with scriptural references and page numbers, is given overleaf.

• copyright
Material in this book is copyright-free provided that it is used for the purpose for which the book is intended. The usual copyright restrictions apply to any use for *commercial* purposes.

Users' Responses
Sales of books in the Palm Tree Press 'Instant Art' series continue to prove that they are meeting a need. The series is now developing in response to, and with the help of, people who have found material in the existing books useful. *Your* ideas or suggestions for new titles would be warmly received and carefully considered!

Contents

Read this story in Genesis 4

Word search

G	T	N	E	M	H	S	I	N	U	P	O
O	C	D	S	C	R	O	P	S	R	O	D
P	B	O	E	F	I	N	K	G	L	R	C
Y	R	G	N	A	C	F	N	F	E	C	F
I	O	L	C	S	B	L	I	H	J	O	L
L	T	I	S	S	H	E	P	R	E	N	O
L	H	K	I	L	L	E	L	A	C	I	O
N	E	N	E	D	H	R	E	M	R	A	F
D	R	T	E	S	O	H	E	P	E	C	S
O	J	E	A	L	O	U	S	M	F	R	B
P	A	B	E	H	E	B	M	R	A	F	E

ABEL   FIELD   KNIFE
ANGRY   FOOL   PUNISHMENT
BROTHER   GOD   SACRIFICE
CAIN   HATE   SHEEP
CROPS   JEALOUS   SHEPHERD
FARMER   KILL   SIN

We must love one another (1 John 3:11)

Draw a line from Cain to his job and Abel to his job

soldier

potter

brickmaker

stone worker

Cain   Abel

farmer

fisherman

shepherd

How many people are on the boat?

The story of Noah is in Genesis 5, 6, 7, 8 and 9

Draw in the other animal in the pair

Word search

ANIMALS	JAPHETH
BOAT	NOAH
DOVE	RAINBOW
FLOOD	RAVEN
HAM	SHEM

J	A	N	I	E	N	O	B
A	W	L	V	M	M	A	H
P	N	O	A	H	J	O	W
H	D	I	B	O	A	T	N
E	O	W	M	N	H	O	E
T	O	O	V	A	I	O	V
H	L	B	M	R	L	A	A
E	F	E	M	E	H	S	R

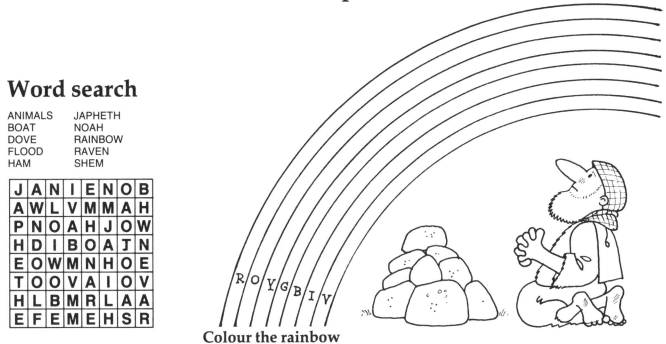

Colour the rainbow

Whenever you see a rainbow, remember God is love
— and will never again flood the earth.

Read the story in Genesis 11

Word search

BABEL
BRICKS
CITY
CONFUSE
LANGUAGE
LORD
TAR
TOWER

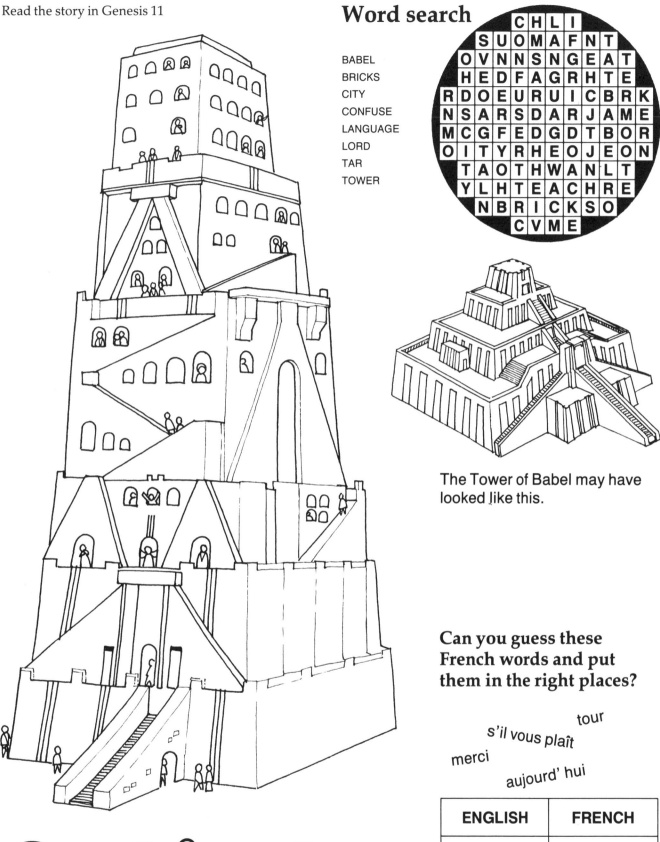

The Tower of Babel may have looked like this.

Can you guess these French words and put them in the right places?

tour
s'il vous plaît
merci
aujourd' hui

ENGLISH	FRENCH
please	
thank you	
today	
tower	

God is the Greatest

Read this story in Genesis 32

Jacob said:

I will not let you go unless you bless me

(Genesis 32:26)

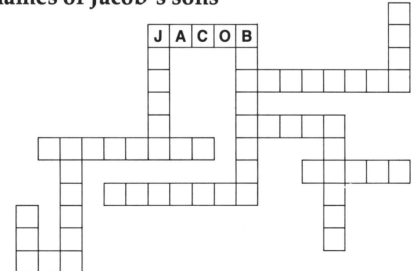

Fill in the names of Jacob's sons

Sons of Jacob and Leah

REUBEN
SIMEON
LEVI
JUDAH
ISSACHAR
ZEBULUN

Sons of Jacob and Rachel

JOSEPH
BENJAMIN

Sons of Jacob and Zilpah

GAD
ASHER

Sons of Jacob and Bilhah

DAN
NAPHTALI

You can find the names
in Genesis 35:22-26

You can find this story in Genesis 37

dream 1

dream 2

Love your brothers and sisters

Colour Joseph's coat

Join up these brothers. The first one is done for you.

James	Cain	Peter	Moses	Esau

Aaron	Jacob	John	Andrew	Abel

Word search

BROTHERS
DOTHAN
DREAM
FLOCKS
JOSEPH
ROBE
SHEAVES
SHEEP
STARS
SUN
WELL
WHEAT

D	R	O	T	S	S	B	E	B	E
N	O	S	T	A	N	R	M	R	J
E	W	H	E	A	T	O	A	O	C
B	E	E	K	V	L	L	S	T	F
D	R	E	A	M	A	E	L	H	S
O	O	P	C	K	P	E	L	E	U
T	B	E	O	H	J	P	H	R	W
H	E	E	F	L	O	C	K	S	B
A	S	L	P	E	S	E	P	H	E
N	U	S	H	O	C	K	S	E	T

Read the story in Genesis 39

Break the code to read the message!

3	10	9	11		5	7	12	4		11	6	4

3	4	12	7	8		1		2	6	1	9	2	4

Ephesians 4:27

a	c	d	e	g	h	i	l	n	o	t	v
1	2	3	4	5	6	7	8	9	10	11	12

Say NO to temptation

Word search

HOUSE   POTIPHAR   SCREAMED
JOSEPH   PRISON   SERVANT
KING   ROBE   SIN

S	T	R	V	A	N	G	T
C	N	S	C	R	N	J	N
R	A	H	P	I	T	O	P
E	V	A	K	V	S	S	H
A	R	I	N	I	S	E	S
M	E	N	R	U	N	P	E
E	S	P	S	O	J	H	J
D	T	E	H	S	B	R	O
E	B	H	O	U	S	E	R

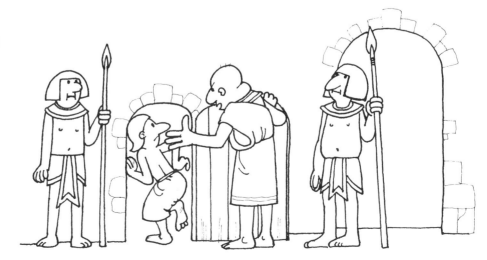

Read the story in Genesis 40 and 41

Chief Baker's Dream

Joseph

Wine Steward's Dream

Pharaoh's Dream

Can you fit these words in?

3 LETTERS
FAT

4 LETTERS
CORN
COWS
THIN

5 LETTERS
BAKER
DREAM
EGYPT
SEVEN
YEARS

6 LETTERS
FAMINE
JOSEPH
PLENTY

7 Years of Plenty

7 Years of Famine

Find the story in Genesis 42-46

Forgive others

(Luke 6:37)

Write down the names of the people in your family:-

Word search

N	I	M	A	J	N	E	B	S	R	A	E	Y	U	B
E	E	G	Y	P	T	M	A	E	R	D	C	L	O	R
R	S	V	A	C	O	N	O	S	E	Y	G	R	I	O
D	R	I	E	N	R	T	Y	S	E	O	T	M	P	N
L	I	V	E	S	T	O	C	K	D	I	N	I	U	R
I	F	Y	A	S	H	E	P	R	O	R	P	S	C	E
H	D	C	F	V	N	E	H	S	O	G	R	S	N	V
C	K	R	E	D	E	V	P	C	F	E	S	I	A	O
J	U	D	A	H	O	I	E	H	H	O	M	N	A	G
S	C	N	O	N	E	L	S	T	E	A	D	G	N	N
O	T	U	H	S	K	C	O	L	F	R	E	A	A	I
S	F	A	T	H	E	R	J	G	O	O	D	B	C	K
O	J	A	C	O	B	Y	O	U	N	G	E	S	T	E

BAG
BENJAMIN
BROTHERS
BUY
CANAAN
CHILDREN
CITY
CORN
CROPS
CUP
DESCENDANTS
DRANK
DREAM

EGYPT
EVIL
FAMINE
FATHER
FLOCKS
FOOD
GOD
GOOD
GOSHEN
GOVERNOR
JACOB
JOSEPH
JUDAH

KING
LIVESTOCK
MISSING
MONEY
NILE
SACK
SEVEN
SHEPHERDS
SON
SPIES
YEARS
YOUNGEST

Find this story in Exodus 1 and 2

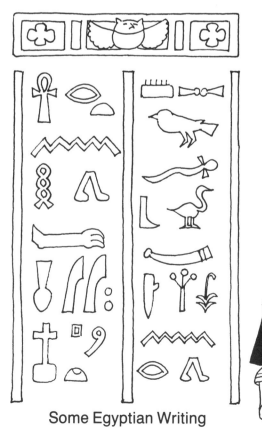

Some Egyptian Writing

See if you can de-code this:

Exodus 2:10

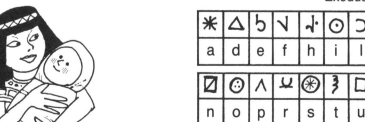

✳	△	▷	⌄	⊹	⊙	⊃	⊙
a	d	e	f	h	i	l	m

⊘	⊙	∧	⊻	✳	⌇	□	⪨
n	o	p	r	s	t	u	w

Moses and the Burning Bush   Palm Tree Worksheet 10

Find this story in Exodus 3

Moses' Excuses

1. I am a nobody.
2. Who will I say has sent me?
3. Suppose they don't believe me?
4. I am a poor speaker.
5. Send someone else!

You can do it Moses

Go to the King of Egypt

I will be with you

(Exodus 3:12)

Lead Moses to the burning bush

Word search

AFRAID   EGYPT   RESCUE
BURNING   GROUND   SANDALS
BUSH   HOLY   SHEEP
DESERT   MOSES

B	U	P	P	E	E	H	S	E	R	T
U	E	R	E	S	C	U	A	G	H	E
H	T	E	G	R	O	U	N	D	E	R
E	P	Y	M	E	E	I	D	P	R	T
D	G	R	O	O	N	E	A	E	S	P
E	I	B	C	R	S	C	L	P	E	Y
S	S	A	U	E	A	E	S	H	E	G
C	O	B	R	S	R	E	S	C	U	E
U	M	T	M	F	H	O	L	Y	P	Y
E	G	Y	P	S	A	F	M	S	A	S

1 BLOOD

2 FROGS

3 GNATS

4 FLIES

5 DEATH OF ANIMALS

6 BOILS

7 HAIL

8 LOCUSTS

9 DARKNESS

10 DEATH OF FIRSTBORN

Find Moses and Aaron's stick in each picture — except one!

This story is in
Exodus chapters 7 to 12

Word search

ANIMALS	DEATH	GNATS
BLOOD	FIRSTBORN	HAIL
BOILS	FLIES	LOCUSTS
DARKNESS	FROGS	MOSES

N	R	O	B	T	S	R	I	F	D
D	S	O	O	L	B	A	B	M	A
M	G	S	T	A	N	G	O	F	R
U	O	H	A	I	L	S	I	R	K
C	R	S	M	S	E	I	L	F	N
S	F	A	E	S	B	O	S	C	E
B	L	O	O	D	E	A	T	H	S
S	T	S	U	C	O	L	F	O	S

Word search

```
B R E I A D A E R B W O O L E
A R O N R O B T S R I F E W N
O M E S D O R L I H N T S E R
S I F T E L U P O R E S T B R
E D O R C B M A L O S R C E E
I N E S L O U S T A E H B O R
R I J T A D I S S O G M H S S
O G F F S Y B O O L E U T T R
G H U C T A O V E M P H E W I
T T U F S S O E E V H H E R T
G P H J U R E R F Y A Y O O P
S E Y S P I I A W O R S C U Y
R U E G P F A S D O A S T E D
O J E S E M A R F R O O D E S
P L O I R S C V E R H P O N S
```

BITTER
BLOOD
BODY
BREAD
CUP
DOORFRAME
EGYPT

FIRE
FIRSTBORN
HERBS
HYSSOP
JESUS
LAMB
LAST SUPPER

MIDNIGHT
PASSOVER
PHARAOH
PLAGUE
REMEMBER
ROASTED
WINE

The story is in Exodus 11 and 12

Break the code to read the message!

Y_ _ _   m_s_   r_m_v_   _h_   _ _ _d
 2 5   5 4   3 2 3   4 3   2 6

y_as_   _f   sin   s_   _ha_   y_ _ _   wi_ _ _   b_
 3 4   2   2   4 4   2 5   6 6   3

_n_ir_ _ _y   p_r_.
 3 4   3 6   5 3

o = 2, e = 3, t = 4,
u = 5, l = 6

Christ, our Passover Lamb has been sacrificed (1 Corinthians 5:7)

Word search

E	P	I	L	L	A	R	A	W
S	G	S	E	S	R	O	H	A
T	L	Y	R	D	E	A	S	T
O	C	M	P	E	G	S	H	E
I	L	R	Y	T	N	T	O	R
R	O	A	M	A	I	R	I	M
A	U	G	N	A	K	A	E	O
H	D	Y	F	D	W	I	N	D
C	H	D	N	A	H	A	E	S

ARMY   FAITH   MOSES
CHARIOTS   HAND   PILLAR
CLOUD   HORSES   RED
DRY   KING   SEA
EAST   LAND   WATER
EGYPTIANS   MIRIAM   WIND

Find this story
in Exodus
14 and 15

By faith the people passed through the Red Sea (Hebrews 11:29)

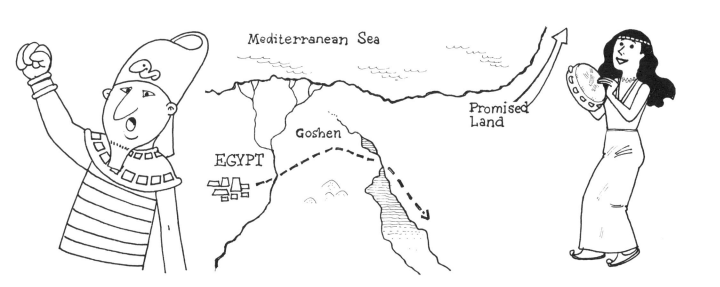

Mediterranean Sea

Promised Land

Goshen

EGYPT

The Ten Commandments are listed in
Exodus 20:1-17 and Deuteronomy 5:1-21

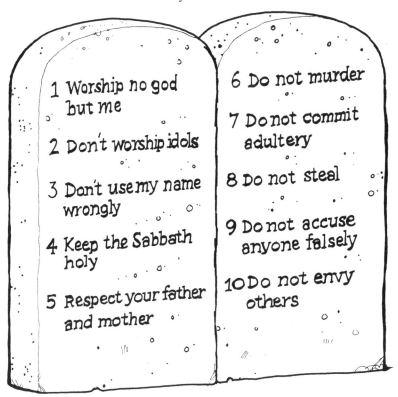

1 Worship no god but me

2 Don't worship idols

3 Don't use my name wrongly

4 Keep the Sabbath holy

5 Respect your father and mother

6 Do not murder

7 Do not commit adultery

8 Do not steal

9 Do not accuse anyone falsely

10 Do not envy others

Which instruction manual belongs to which item?

I will put my laws in their hearts

(Hebrews 10:16)

Jesus explained these laws in Matthew 5:17-48

1. These can become our 'gods'
2. Be careful about making idols
3. Watch your language
4. I haven't got time for worship
5. Respect your Parents
6. Hateful words are like murder
7. Be careful about your thoughts
8. Don't steal
9. Be careful who you accuse
10. Don't covet

Read the story in Exodus 32

Which way up the mountain?

Don't make idols

(Exodus 20:4)

What you spend your time and money on can become an idol.

Word search

A	E	M	O	S	E	S	G	O	I
A	N	I	D	L	A	T	L	D	G
R	M	G	O	A	R	O	O	N	S
N	G	R	R	E	R	N	I	O	T
O	E	O	G	Y	I	C	R	Y	O
B	N	M	O	U	N	T	A	I	N
A	U	E	L	A	G	O	L	D	E
D	G	L	D	E	S	T	R	O	Y
N	B	I	L	T	A	I	N	L	S
E	C	I	F	I	R	C	A	S	Y

AARON   DESTROY   MOSES
ANGRY   EARRINGS   MOUNTAIN
BULL   GOLD   SACRIFICE
DANCING   IDOLS   STONE

Are any of these your idols?

Moses and the Spies

Read this story in Numbers 13

How many happy spies can you see? ☐

Put a ring around those things which you think the spies might have taken with them

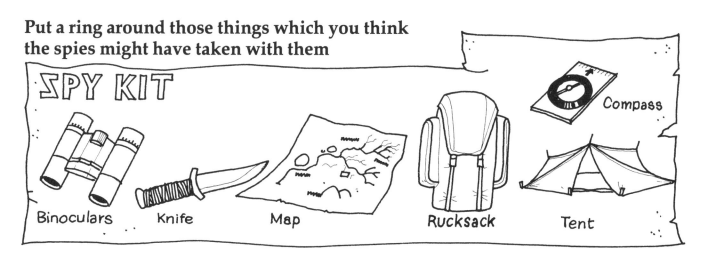

SPY KIT

Binoculars   Knife   Map   Rucksack   Compass   Tent

Different kinds of fruit

3 LETTERS
FIG

4 LETTERS
DATE
PEAR
PLUM

5 LETTERS
APPLE
GRAPE
LEMON
MANGO
MELON
PEACH

6 LETTERS
BANANA
CHERRY
ORANGE

7 LETTERS
AVOCADO

10 LETTERS
STRAWBERRY

11 LETTERS
POMEGRANATE

Read this story in Joshua 6

...and the walls collapsed

(Joshua 6:20)

Rescue route

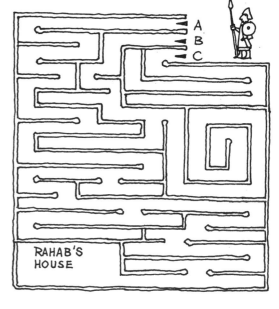

Word search

T	R	U	M	P	E	T	S	E	P
I	N	J	O	S	H	U	A	T	R
C	O	A	E	M	A	R	C	H	I
Y	W	T	N	R	N	E	A	X	E
I	A	S	R	E	I	D	L	O	S
G	L	R	V	O	V	C	X	B	T
A	L	E	M	T	U	O	H	S	S
O	S	G	D	Y	T	I	C	O	B

ARMY   PRIESTS
BOX   SEVEN
CITY   SHOUT
COVENANT   SOLDIERS
GATES   TRUMPETS
JERICHO   WALLS
JOSHUA
MARCH

RAHAB'S HOUSE

Which is the rescue route to Rahab's House? ☐

Read the story in Joshua 7

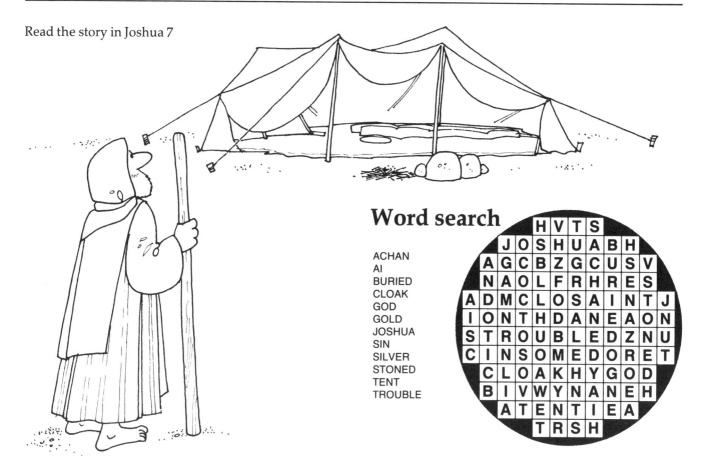

Word search

ACHAN
AI
BURIED
CLOAK
GOD
GOLD
JOSHUA
SIN
SILVER
STONED
TENT
TROUBLE

```
    H V T S
  J O S H U A B H
A G C B Z G C U S V
N A O L F R H R E S
A D M C L O S A I N T J
I O N T H D A N E A O N
S T R O U B L E D Z N U
C I N S O M E D O R E T
C L O A K H Y G O D
B I V W Y N A N E H
  A T E N T I E A
    T R S H
```

EH SWONK EHT STERCES FO EHT TRAEH

___ _____ ___ ____ _____ ___ ___ _____

The words are written backwards — unjumble them

Psalm 44:21

Here are other ways of being dishonest:-

Keeping things you find

Pretending

Cheating in a test

Playing games unfairly

Keeping the change

Taking sweets without asking

Bringing home school pencils

1   2   3

Find the way to Achan's tent

For there is nothing that God cannot do (Luke 1:37)

Word search

ARMY	JOSHUA	STILL
GIBEON	MOON	SUN
HAILSTONES	PANIC	TROOPS

The day the Sun and the Moon stood still

Find this story in Joshua 10

Colour these powerful things, but remember: Our God is more powerful than any of these

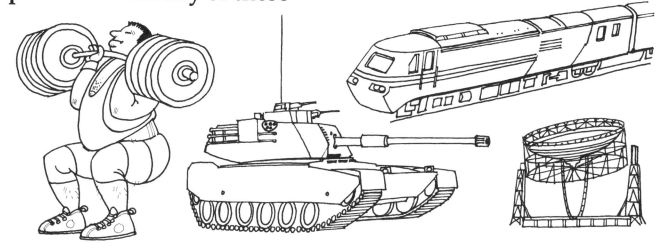

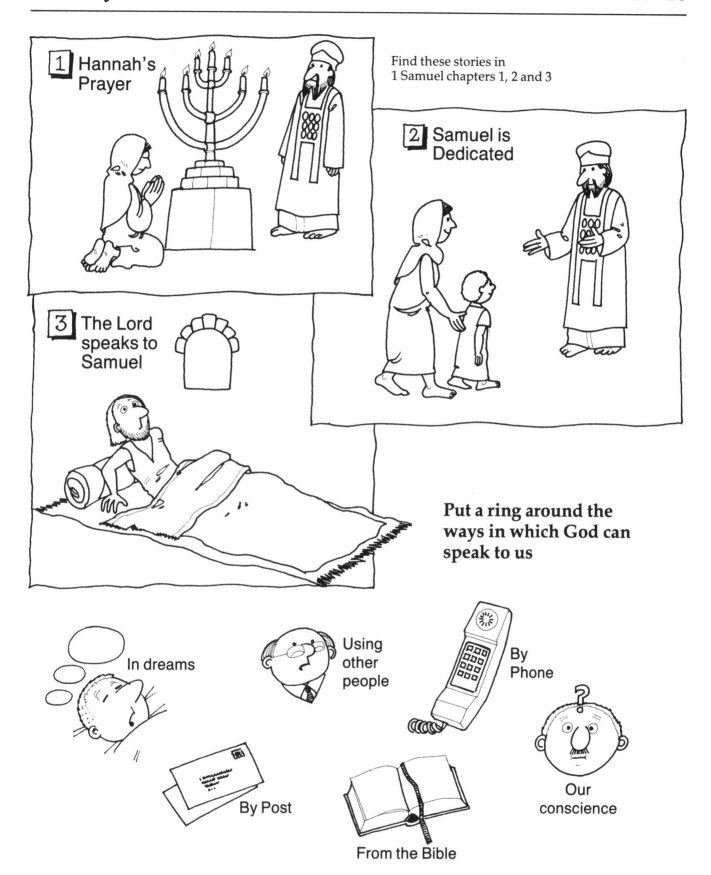

1 Hannah's Prayer

Find these stories in 1 Samuel chapters 1, 2 and 3

2 Samuel is Dedicated

3 The Lord speaks to Samuel

Put a ring around the ways in which God can speak to us

In dreams

Using other people

By Phone

By Post

From the Bible

Our conscience

Speak Lord, your servant is listening (1 Samuel 3:9)

Naaman

Read 2 Kings 5

Naaman's Wife's Servant
(God can use you too!)

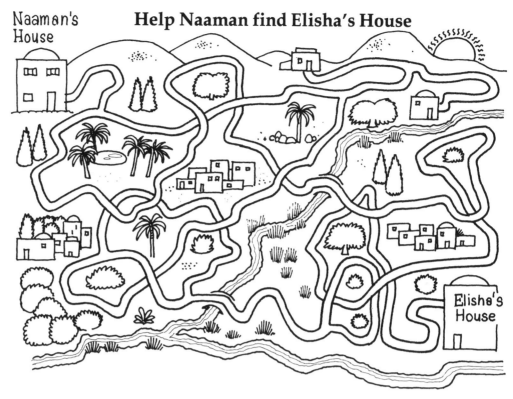

Naaman's House

Help Naaman find Elisha's House

Elisha's House

Word search

E	C	N	S	F	L	E	S	H
D	O	U	A	L	S	G	E	G
A	Y	M	R	A	G	E	V	I
J	Z	I	E	E	M	H	E	F
O	G	S	E	R	V	A	N	T
R	I	V	E	R	K	Z	N	E
D	O	G	A	H	S	I	L	E
A	I	S	R	A	E	L	N	O
N	T	E	H	P	O	R	P	G

ARMY
CURE
DISEASE
ELISHA
FLESH
GEHAZI
GIFT
GIRL
GOD

ISRAEL
JORDAN
KING
NAAMAN
PROPHET
RAGE
RIVER
SERVANT
SEVEN

Can you make 10 or more words from SERVANT ?

Read the story in Daniel 1

Draw the faces of Daniel and his friends

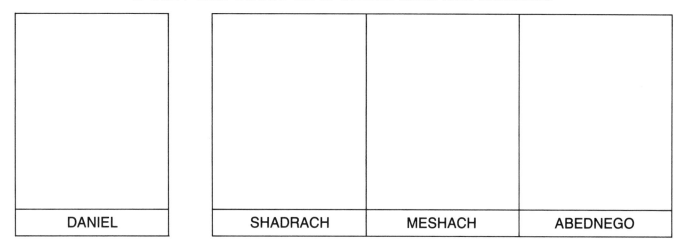

| DANIEL | SHADRACH | MESHACH | ABEDNEGO |

Can you fit these words in the boxes?

3 LETTERS
PEA

4 LETTERS
BEAN
LEEK

6 LETTERS
CARROT
CELERY
POTATO
RADISH

7 LETTERS
LETTUCE
PARSNIP
SPINACH

8 LETTERS
BROCCOLI
CUCUMBER

11 LETTERS
CAULIFLOWER

Put a ring around those foods Daniel and his friends were allowed to eat

Beans

Water

WINE

How many words can you make from BELTESHAZZAR ?

Say NO to doing wrong

Read the story in Daniel 3

Jesus said: "I will be with you always." (Matthew 28:20)

Word search

H	D	E	N	D	C	G	W
C	T	D	W	G	O	O	O
A	G	O	K	I	N	G	R
R	B	M	H	N	E	L	S
D	W	E	R	I	F	C	H
A	C	S	D	R	E	D	I
H	L	H	S	N	U	L	P
S	T	A	T	U	E	O	G
A	H	C	F	T	E	G	F
S	E	H	T	O	L	C	O

ABEDNEGO
BOW
CLOTHES
FIRE
FOUR
GOD
GOLD
HOT
KING
MESHACH
SHADRACH
STATUE
WORSHIP

Which are the odd ones out?

Will you be the odd one out if necessary and still worship God?

Read the story in Daniel 4

Do not be proud

(Romans 12:16)

Word search

ANIMALS
BIRDS
CHOP
DANIEL
DEW
DREAM
FRUIT
GRASS
HUMBLE
IRON
NEBUCHADNEZZAR
PROUD
SEVEN
STUMP
TREE

Help King Neb find his palace

Read the story in Daniel 5

Belshazzar's Feast

Word search

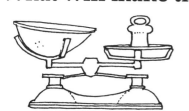

BELSHAZZAR
CUPS
DANIEL
DIVISIONS
DRINKING

FEAST
GOLD
HAND
KING

NUMBER
WALL
WEIGHT
WRITING

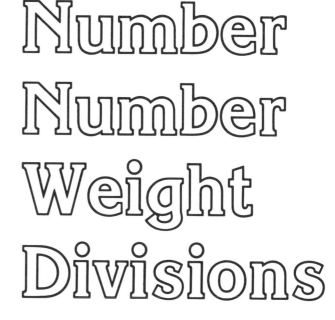

Number
Number
Weight
Divisions

What will make these balance?

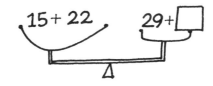

$15 + 22$ $29 + \square$

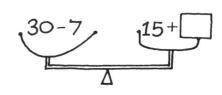

$30 - 7$ $15 + \square$

He prayed to God three times a day

Read the story in Daniel 6

Help Daniel find his way out of the lions den

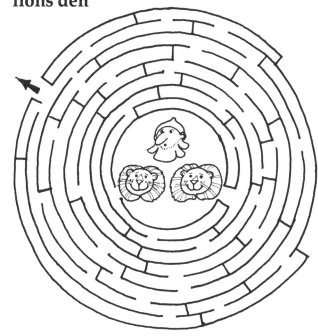

Find the words from the verses in the story and write the letters in the boxes:

1. The King's name: verse 1

2. Daniel did this 3 times a day: verse 10

3. These opened towards Jerusalem: verse 10

4. The King spent a sleepless one: verse 18

5. This shut the lion's mouth: verse 22

6. Daniel was rescued from the: verse 22

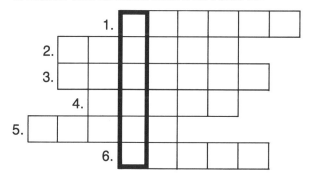

Read the story in Luke 1

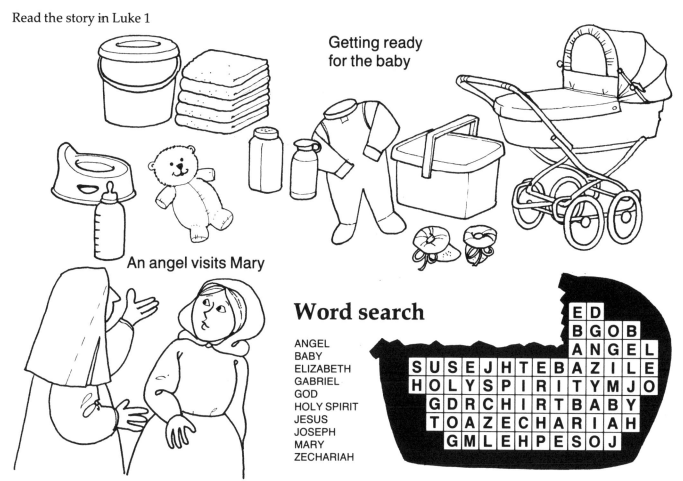

Getting ready for the baby

An angel visits Mary

Word search

ANGEL
BABY
ELIZABETH
GABRIEL
GOD
HOLY SPIRIT
JESUS
JOSEPH
MARY
ZECHARIAH

```
          E D
          B G O B
          A N G E L
S U S E J H T E B A Z I L E
H O L Y S P I R I T Y M J O
  G D R C H I R T B A B Y
T O A Z E C H A R I A H
  G M L E H P E S O J
```

For there is nothing that God cannot do (Luke 1:37)

Help Mary find Elizabeth by answering the questions correctly

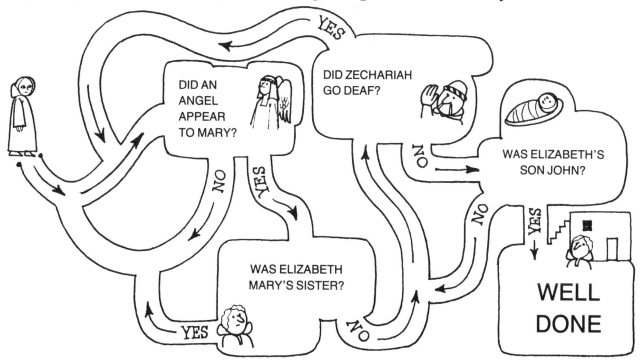

DID AN ANGEL APPEAR TO MARY?

DID ZECHARIAH GO DEAF?

WAS ELIZABETH'S SON JOHN?

WAS ELIZABETH MARY'S SISTER?

WELL DONE

Read the story in Luke 2 and Matthew 2

We have come to worship him

(Matthew 1:2)

Word search

ANGELS
BETHLEHEM
CHILD
EAST

HEROD
KING
MANGER
MARY

	O	E		
	F	G		
T	E	I	R	
N	G	I	F	T	S	E	S	H	E	R	O	D	R	E	B
E	Y	R	A	M	H	N	O	D	L	I	H	C	H
B	E	T	H	L	E	H	E	M	D	S	B
E	G	I	M	A	C	P	C	E	I	S	O
N	G	S	I	N	S	H	N	L	G
E	A	T	D	L	I	N	G	E	L	O	H
M	M	G	N	I	K	I	G	I	R	L	Y
A	S	T	R	A	Y	N	N	O	N	G	D	E	B
N	M	Y	R	R	H	G	A	K	F	R	A	T	S	C	I
	R	R	Y	H	
	F	S	O	
	O	E	

FIELDS
FRANKINCENSE
GIFTS
GOLD

MYRRH
SHEPHERDS
SINGING
STAR

Read the story in Luke 2:22-38

Word search

```
C H I D L N T F T S A N T S
J E R U S A L E M U J I E I
E E S A N K I O M S E P L M
L O S N O G E D O P S A T I
U S A U H W L M W E L R K S
M D O T S I W E S I M E O N
E C H I H D T H A L E N E T
L I M C E O S K N A H T S I
T A N E O W G H T S I S E W
```

ANNA	JESUS	TEMPLE
CHILD	PARENTS	THANKS
EIGHT	SIMEON	WIDOW
JERUSALEM		

Help Anna find Simeon and Jesus

Anna

Simeon

Use the code ⌐ = i, ∨ = o etc to find out what this says:-

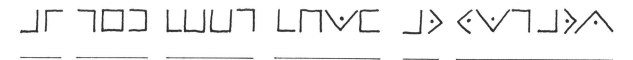

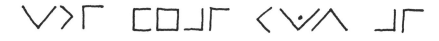

Habakkuk 2:3

Read the story in Luke 2:41-52

Jesus grew both in

Put the first letter of the picture in each box

 and

and gaining favour with God and men

(Luke 2:52)

Help Mary and Joseph find Jesus in the temple

AMAZED
BOY
DAY
FATHERS
HOUSE
JERUSALEM
JESUS
MOTHER
PARENTS
QUESTIONS
TEMPLE
TWELVE
WISDOM
WORRIED

Word search

T	R	M	O	T	H	E	R	M	I
W	O	E	Y	B	L	V	E	S	W
T	H	J	D	O	L	L	W	Q	O
E	E	W	E	Y	A	E	J	U	M
E	M	O	D	S	I	W	S	E	Z
V	O	R	U	Q	U	T	R	S	A
P	A	R	E	N	T	S	E	T	M
L	E	I	E	S	U	O	H	I	A
J	T	E	M	P	L	E	T	O	J
Y	A	D	E	Z	A	M	A	N	E
E	M	O	D	H	T	A	F	S	H

Read the story in Luke 5:1-11

There are 6 fish hidden in the picture. Can you find them?

They left everything and followed Jesus

(Luke 5:11)

See if you can fit in the names of the disciples:-

ANDREW
BARTHOLOMEW
JAMES

JAMES
JOHN
JUDAS

MATTHEW
PETER
PHILIP

SIMON
THADDAEUS
THOMAS

These names are listed in Matthew 10:2-4

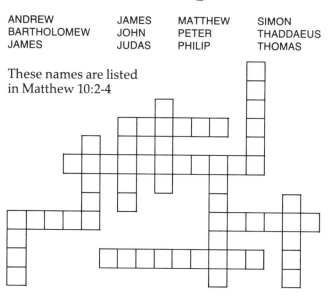

Write down the names of your best friends

The Bible tells us to be careful in choosing our friends.

Wedding at Cana

Read this story in John 2

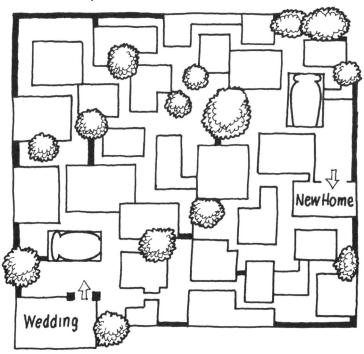

Follow the route through the village to the couple's new home

Do whatever he tells you

(John 2:5)

See if you can find six water jars on this page

Word search

BANQUET
BEST
CANA
DISCIPLES
JESUS
MIRACLES
MOTHER
SERVANTS
SIX
THIRTY
TWENTY
WATER JARS
WEDDING
WINE

The Paralysed Man Healed

Palm Tree Worksheet 33

Find this story in Mark 2:1-12

Word search

P	L	A	M	E	R	S	H	I	N
W	A	L	K	A	T	T	F	D	E
A	O	R	G	M	I	S	O	B	E
S	I	O	A	A	E	O	R	O	S
T	V	T	F	L	R	O	G	N	E
E	F	O	O	R	Y	R	I	O	D
W	A	H	U	E	M	S	V	O	G
I	A	V	R	E	E	N	E	M	O
D	E	L	E	G	I	V	N	D	V
R	P	E	M	S	O	O	L	E	I
S	A	L	K	S	W	A	M	T	E

DOOR
FAITH
FORGIVEN
FOUR
HOLE
MAT
MEN
PARALYSED
ROOF
SINS
WALK

Fill in the words from this box:

walk	roof	sins	mat

1. The hole was in the __ __ __ __ .

2. The man was lying on a __ __ __ .

3. Jesus said, ''Your __ __ __ __ are forgiven.''

4. Jesus said, ''Pick up your mat and __ __ __ __ .''

Find this story in Luke 8

The seed is like the word of God

Word search

T	U	N	S	T	N	A	L	P
E	O	W	D	R	U	I	S	A
S	D	E	E	S	S	D	E	T
E	N	E	E	O	R	E	T	H
G	U	N	W	I	B	V	R	S
F	O	E	B	L	D	I	O	O
R	R	O	K	Y	C	L	C	W
U	G	W	D	H	B	F	K	N
I	U	I	E	E	S	R	Y	E
T	I	S	N	R	O	H	T	D

BIRDS   PATH   SOIL
DEVIL   PLANTS   SOWER
FRUIT   RICHES   THORNS
GOOD   ROCKY   WEEDS
GROUND   SEEDS

The Path	Rocky Ground
The message taken away	Time of testing
The weeds and thorns	**The Good Soil**
Worries and Riches	Good Fruit

Which sort of ground are you?

Read this story in
Matthew 14:13-21

It's also in
  Mark 6
  Luke 9
  John 6

Jesus makes a lot out of a little given to him

Can you fit these words into the boxes?

3 LETTERS
  BOY
  SEA
  TWO

4 LETTERS
  FISH
  FIVE

5 LETTERS
  BREAD
  GRASS

6 LETTERS
  CROWDS
  LOAVES
  PEOPLE
  TWELVE

7 LETTERS
  BASKETS
  GALILEE

8 LETTERS
  MOUNTAIN

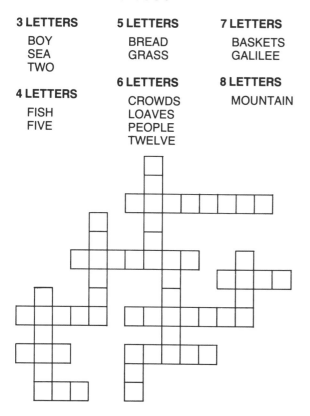

Put a circle around the numbers which are in the story

Find this story in Matthew 14:22-32

Trust in the Lord with all your heart

(Proverbs 3:5)

Word search

DOUBT FORGIVEN WAVES
FAITH PETER WATER
FEAR ROCK WET
FEET WALK

G	K	T	E	R	V	B	E	C	D
E	F	A	I	T	H	G	K	W	T
P	E	F	O	W	K	F	E	A	R
K	C	F	T	A	B	O	U	V	O
Y	T	P	E	T	E	R	S	E	B
W	A	E	N	E	U	G	K	S	T
N	V	R	A	R	T	I	L	R	B
B	P	O	T	B	S	V	A	D	U
K	T	C	D	E	T	E	W	E	O
E	N	K	W	A	B	N	U	O	D

Which hand helps Peter?

Read this story in Luke 8

Even the winds and waves obey him

(Matthew 8:27)

Word search

ASLEEP	OBEY
BOAT	QUIET
CALM	SIDE
DISCIPLES	STILL
FAITH	STORM
JESUS	WAVES
LAKE	WIND

```
M R O B E Y J E P E E L S A B F O
S T O R M E V A W D T E K A L
W A V E S E L P I C S I D
T E I U Q E L S N T E
I Q S M L A C H D
```

Draw a circle around those things you might find at the sea-side

Find this story in John 9

I was blind

but now I see

(John 9:25)

Word search

T	H	G	I	S	Y	U	D	F
A	S	N	I	S	E	I	F	S
B	L	I	N	D	U	E	A	E
L	O	G	L	O	Y	S	C	Y
I	O	G	B	O	R	N	E	E
N	P	E	H	S	A	W	H	J
B	O	B	T	D	U	M	E	S

BEGGING   SEE
BLIND   SIGHT
BORN   SILOAM
EYES   SINS
FACE   WASH
JESUS
MUD
POOL

Use your eyes and count how many naughty children there are here ☐

Read the story in John 12:1-8

The perfume filled the house

(John 12:3)

Tick the smells you like

☐ Fish and Chips	☐ After Shave
☐ Petrol	☐ Smoke
☐ Roses	☐ The Sea
☐ Banana	☐ Burnt Toast

Word search

BETHANY   MONEY
DINNER   NARD
FEET   PERFUME
HAIR   POOR
HOUSE   POURED
JESUS   SMELL
LAZARUS   SOLD
MARTHA   TABLE
MARY   WIPED

S	U	S	E	J	E	E	L	D	L	M
M	E	P	S	S	M	A	R	Y	A	O
E	O	O	U	U	Z	A	H	R	Y	N
L	L	O	F	A	N	L	R	N	A	E
D	H	R	R	E	L	B	A	T	H	Y
E	E	U	F	E	E	H	E	N	H	Z
P	S	O	M	T	T	T	S	A	W	A
I	H	S	R	E	N	N	I	D	I	L
W	T	E	B	D	E	R	U	O	P	E

Are you mean or generous with your giving?

Be extravagant giving to God

Find this story in Matthew 25

Word search

ASLEEP
BRIDEGROOM
CONTAINERS
CRY
FIVE
FOOLISH
FULL
GIRLS
KINGDOM
LAMPS

LATE
MEET
MIDNIGHT
OIL
READY
SHOP
TEN
TRIMMED
WEDDING
WISE

A	S	L	E	E	V	I	F	E	O	I
E	H	F	A	T	E	O	W	P	Y	B
V	O	C	U	A	O	N	E	T	R	T
S	P	M	A	L	I	E	D	I	C	R
I	M	G	I	R	L	S	D	G	O	I
W	I	S	E	S	T	E	I	K	Y	M
I	H	A	A	E	G	L	N	I	D	M
E	D	D	E	R	S	I	G	N	A	E
T	R	M	O	D	G	N	I	K	E	D
S	C	O	N	T	A	I	N	E	R	S
E	M	I	D	N	I	G	H	T	E	D

How many wise bridesmaids?

How many foolish bridesmaids?

You will find this story in Mark 12:41-44 and Luke 21:1-4

God loves a cheerful giver

(2 Corinthians 9:7)

Money in New Testament Times

Jewish	Roman	British
1 lepton		15p
2 lepta	1 quadran	30p
	4 quadrans = 1 as	£1·25
	16 as = 1 denarius	£20·00

A Tithe God's Part

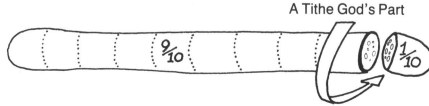

9/10   1/10

Word search

CHEERFUL   PROUD
COINS   RICH
COPPER   SACRIFICE
GIVE   TEMPLE
HUMBLE   TITHE
MONEY   TREASURY
POOR   WIDOW

N	S	L	C	I	N	S	E	E	W
O	A	U	O	D	O	N	V	I	G
T	C	F	E	H	W	I	D	E	R
I	R	R	G	C	M	O	N	E	Y
T	I	E	F	I	W	C	P	L	E
H	F	E	A	R	V	P	O	B	N
E	I	H	E	S	O	E	U	M	O
S	C	C	F	C	U	O	D	U	O
I	E	R	D	U	O	R	P	H	R
P	T	E	M	P	L	E	Y	Y	E

Spot the 10 differences: Find this story in John 11

Jesus said:-

I am the

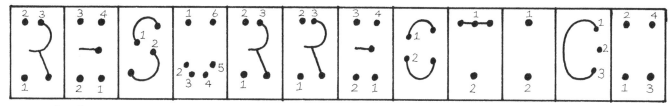

and the

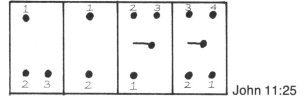

John 11:25

Draw in the faces of the people when they saw Lazarus come out of the tomb

Who were Lazarus' sisters?

M _ _ _ _ and M _ _ _ _ _ _ _

Which way? ☐

Who else was raised from the dead? _ _ _ _ _ _ _

Pentecost

Find this story in Acts 2

Hours

AFRAID ⟶ then ⟶ BRAVE

Word search

```
H A H E L P E R D
E G O J M P S V E
A F L A M E S V Y
V B Y E H K A N Q
E T S W Z R C F P
N I P L B O O R R
U X I A D G J O O
J E R U S A L E M
E M I P S F E V I
S Y T B E R H K S
U N Q T I A W Z E
S C F F I I L O R
U X W I N D A D G
```

AFRAID
BRAVE
FIRE
FLAMES
HEAVEN
HELPER
HOLY SPIRIT
JERUSALEM
JESUS
PROMISE
ROOM
WIND

The Holy Spirit helps us to:

Tell Others

Understand the Bible

Know what to do

Be Joyful

Read this story in Acts 3

Can you make at least 10 words from BEAUTIFUL ?

Healed

Can you pair up these feet?

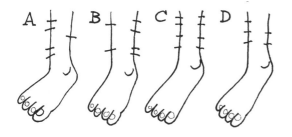

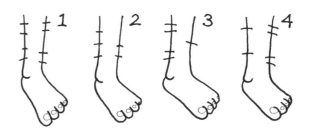

Word search

H	T	G	N	E	R	T	S	H	O	A
T	W	A	L	K	E	D	P	G	B	N
J	M	N	M	P	R	G	R	E	E	K
E	M	S	E	L	K	N	A	G	G	L
S	P	E	T	E	R	U	Y	T	G	Y
U	J	H	E	H	T	E	E	H	E	E
S	L	R	E	I	H	M	R	R	D	N
W	H	S	F	A	P	A	J	E	H	O
T	W	U	N	L	S	L	E	O	D	M
A	L	D	E	P	M	U	J	O	W	B
P	R	A	I	S	I	N	G	G	E	B

ANKLES	LAME
BEAUTIFUL	MONEY
BEGGED	NAME
FEET	PETER
GATE	PRAISING
GOD	PRAYER
HAND	STRENGTH
HELP	TEMPLE
JESUS	THREE
JOHN	WALKED
JUMPED	

Read this story in Acts 7:54-60

His Spirit fills us with

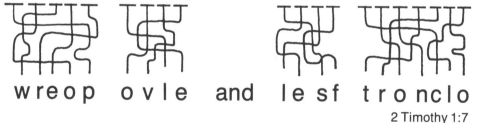

wreop   ovle   and   le sf   tronclo

2 Timothy 1:7

Word search

ANGER   HOLY SPIRIT
CITY   JESUS
CLOAKS   KNELT
CRY   SAUL
GLORY   STEPHEN
HEAVEN   STONING

Who was holding the cloaks? Find his name by putting the first letter of each picture in the empty box

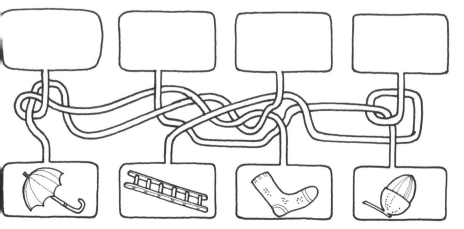

C	R	R	E	G	N	A	E
R	L	H	L	N	C	G	I
C	A	O	T	Y	L	S	T
S	R	L	O	U	O	U	S
Y	N	Y	A	K	A	S	Y
J	E	S	U	S	K	H	P
S	H	P	J	E	S	E	I
A	P	I	G	T	N	A	R
U	E	R	P	L	I	V	I
Y	T	I	C	E	G	E	T
H	S	T	O	N	I	N	G
E	A	V	N	K	E	L	T

Find this story in Acts 12

1 Peter asleep

2 Friends pray

3 Peter awoken

4 Gates open

5 Peter knocks

6 Friends happy

The prayer of a good person has a powerful effect (James 5:16)

Help Peter find his friends